Gold Classics

Frank Sinatra

Wise Publications
London/New York/Paris/Sydney/Copenhagen/Madrid/Tokyo

Angel Eyes

Words by Earl Brent
Music by Matt Dennis

Slowly

N.C.

Try to think— that love's not a-round,— still it's un-com-fort-'bly near,—

— my old heart— ain't gain-in' no ground— be-

Come Fly With Me

Words by Sammy Cahn
Music by James Van Heusen

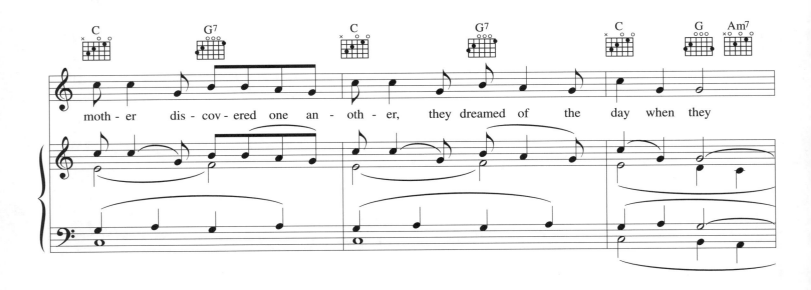

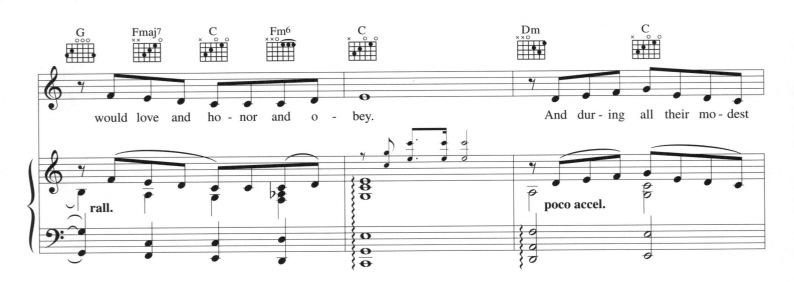

East Of The Sun (And West Of The Moon)

Words & Music by Brooks Bowman

Slowly

wish that we could live up in the sky,_____ where we could find a place a-way up

stars we'll find a har-mo-ny of life to a love-ly tune,

east of the sun and west of the moon,

dear, east of the sun and west of the

moon. moon.

I'll Never Smile Again, Until I Smile At You

Words & Music by Ruth Lowe

Moderato, with expression

I've Got You Under My Skin

Words & Music by Cole Porter

21

I'd sa - cri - fice an - y - thing, come what might, for the sake of hav - ing you

near, in spite of a warn - ing voice that comes in the night and re - peats and re - peats in my

ear: "Don't you know, lit - tle fool, you nev - er can

win, use your men - ta - li - ty, wake up to re -

a - li - ty." But each time I do, just the thought of you makes me

stop, be-fore I be - gin, 'cause I've got you un - der my

skin. I've

If I Had You

Words & Music by Ted Shapiro, Jimmy Campbell & Reg Connelly

CHORUS (with expression)

pals, I'd nev - er mind, I could start my life all a -

new if I had you.

I could climb the snow capp'd moun - tains, sail the might - y o - cean

wide, I could cross the burn - ing de - sert,

It's Nice To Go Trav'ling

Words by Sammy Cahn
Music by James Van Heusen

Repeat to fade

Verse 2:
You will find the Maedchen
And the gay Muchachas are rare
But they can't compare with the sexy line
That parades each day at Sunset and Vine.
It's quite the life to play gypsy
And roam as gypsies will roam
But your heart starts singing
When you're homeward winging 'cross the foam.
And the Hudson river
Makes you start to quiver
Like the latest flivver
That simply is dripping with chrome.

It's nice to go trav'ling
But it's oh so nice to come home!

The Lady Is A Tramp

Words by Lorenz Hart
Music by Richard Rodgers

She nev - er both - ers with
Won't dish the dirt with

peo - ple she hates,—— that's why the la - dy is a
rest of the girls,—— that's why the la - dy is a

1. tramp.————

2. tramp.———— She likes the

free, fresh wind in her hair,——

The Night We Called It A Day

Words by Tom Adair
Music by Matt Dennis

My Way

Original Words & Music by Claude Francois, Jacques Revaux & Gilles Thibaut
English Words by Paul Anka

42

Oh Look At Me Now

Words by John DeVries
Music by Joe Bushkin

Moderately

For I'm not the guy who cared a-bout love, and I'm not the guy who cared a-bout for - tunes and such, nev-er cared much, but, look at me now.

Somethin' Stupid

Words & Music by C. Carson Parks

Moderately slow

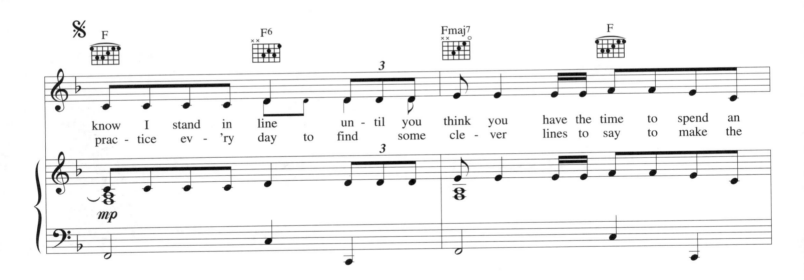

know I stand in line un - til you think you have the time to spend an
prac - tice ev - 'ry day to find some cle - ver lines to say to make the

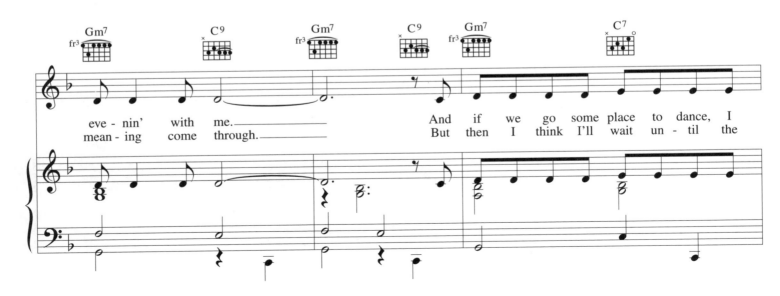

eve - nin' with me.
mean - ing come through.

And if we go some place to dance, I
But then I think I'll wait un - til the

47

Strangers In The Night

Words by Charles Singleton & Eddie Snyder
Music by Bert Kaempfert

Beguine tempo

Stran-gers in the night exchang-ing glan-ces, won-d'ring in the night what were the chan-ces we'd be shar-ing love be-fore the night was

through._____ Some-thing in your eyes_____ was so in - vi -ting,

some-thing in your smile_____ was so ex - ci -ting, some-thing in my heart_____ told me I must have

you._____ Stran -gers in the night,_____ two lone -ly peo -ple, we were

stran -gers in the night,_____ up to the mo - ment when we said our first hel - lo,

lit-tle did we know love was just a glance a - way, a warm em - bra - cing dance a - way and

ev - er since that night___ we've been to - geth - er, lov - ers at first sight,___ in love for - ev - er,

it turned out so right,___ for stran-gers in the night.___

night.___

The Very Thought Of You

Words & Music by Ray Noble

I don't need your pho-to-graph, _____ to keep_ by my bed;
I hold you re-spon-si-ble, _____ I'll take_ it to law,

Your pic - ture is al - ways in __ my head. _____
I nev - er have felt like this __ be - fore. _____

I don't need your por-trait, dear, _____ to call _ you to mind, _____
I'm su - ing for dam-ag - es, _____ ex-cus - es won't do, _____

_ for sleep - ing or wak-ing, dear, _ I find; _____
_ I'll on - ly be sat-is - fied _ with you; _____

poco rit.

Refrain

The ver - y thought of you, _____ and I for-get to do, _____

_____ the lit - tle or - di - na - ry things that ev'-ry-one

ought to do._____ I'm liv - ing in a kind of day - dream, I'm

hap - py as a king, and fool - ish tho' it may seem, to

me _____ that's ev' - ry - thing. _____ The mere i - dea of you,_____

_____ the long - ing here for you, _____ you'll nev - er

Exclusive distributors:
Music Sales Limited
8/9 Frith Street,
London W1V 5TZ, England.
Music Sales Pty Limited
120 Rothschild Avenue
Rosebery, NSW 2018,
Australia.

Order No. AM965767
ISBN 0-7119-8337-2
This book © Copyright 2000 by Wise Publications

Book design by Phil Levene
Compiled by Pete Evans

Photograph courtesy of London Features International

Printed in the United Kingdom by
Caligraving Limited, Thetford, Norfolk.

Your Guarantee of Quality
As publishers, we strive to produce every
book to the highest commercial standards.
The music has been freshly engraved and the book has
been carefully designed to minimise awkward page turns
and to make playing from it a real pleasure. Particular care
has been given to specifying acid-free, neutral-sized
paper made from pulps which have not been
elemental chlorine bleached. This pulp is from farmed
sustainable forests and was produced with special regard
for the environment. Throughout, the printing and
binding have been planned to ensure a sturdy, attractive
publication which should give years of enjoyment.
If your copy fails to meet our high standards,
please inform us and we will gladly replace it.

Music Sales' complete catalogue describes thousands
of titles and is available in full colour sections by subject,
direct from Music Sales Limited. Please state your areas of interest
and send a cheque/postal order for £1.50 for postage to:
Music Sales Limited, Newmarket Road, Bury St. Edmunds,
Suffolk IP33 3YB.

www.musicsales.com